Dolphin Head

Myrtle Bank -

Old Fort Pub

Skull Creek

Indian
Shell Ring

Hudsons -
The Landings

ndmill
rbour -

Middens

Port Royal Sound

Hilton Head
Plantation

Honey Horn
Plantation

Main Street

Beach City

Fish Haul
Plantation

Fort Walker

Baynard
Mausoleum

Port Royal
Plantation

Hotel
Intercontinental

William Hilton Parkway

Palmetto Dunes

Hyatt
Regency

Mariner's
Inn

Marriott
Resort

Atlantic Ocean

Copyright 1987 by SouthArt, Inc.
First Edition Library of Congress Catalogue
card number 87- 060225. All rights reserved.

Printed in Switzerland by Vontobel, Feldmeilen/Zurich,
Switzerland

ISBN # 0- 9610698- 1- 3

Discovering

Hilton Head Island

A View of Nature's Wonders

Text by
Margaret Greer
Photography by
William Cornelia

INTRODUCTION

When someone learns that I have lived full time on Hilton Head Island for over twenty-five years, the fact elicits one or the other of two comments: "You must be a native," or "You've seen a lot of changes since you first came." To the first statement I respond, "No. Natives, people who are born here, are sometimes third and fourth generation Islanders. They are familiar with the melodic cadence of Gullah and can remember when, as one put it, 'You could park a wagonload of gold overnight at the crossroads and no one would touch it.' "

To the second declaration ("You've seen a lot of changes since you first came") I reply, "Yes and no." (About fifteen years ago, we began locking our doors and removing the keys from the car ignition, but that's another story.) "Yes, the population has grown twentyfold and hosts hundreds of thousands of visitors every year. Swamps have been drained for housing and golf courses; multi-storied hotels provide havens for tourists; and services and small businesses bring permanent young families to satisfy the needs of a growing community.

"Analysis of these changes reveals some hidden benefits. By draining swamps and follies, the voracious mosquito has been reduced to where one isn't bitten fifty times a minute as previously experienced, and open spaces on golf courses let in sunlight necessary for the growth of vegetation which, in turn, supplies more grasses and seeds for birds and animals. The young families who can now make Hilton Head Island their home bring an enthusiasm and energy necessary for better communities."

The shape of the Island has altered as the beaches persistently move southward with currents nibbling away on the north side of the Island and spewing the sand at the south end. The ecology has changed little. The alligator and the opposum, the deer and the raccoon have seen human habitation pass from Indian to planter to pirate to slave to soldier to hunter to developer to today's potpourri. The tide ebbs and flows, moving forward each day by fifty minutes. Shrimp, oysters, fish, feeding birds and spartina grass adjust their cycles accordingly.

Some people have long considered islands and escape synonymous. Novelists explore the search for tranquility in a setting of palm trees. Evolutionary theory explains our homing to the Sea. With the wars of the world and televised violence devaluing life, shock has been pushed deep into the corners of minds. The search for tranquility has become more urgent.

With photographs by Bill Cornelia, who has probed the small unknowns as well as the big picture for many years here and elsewhere, this book should energize your own camera, your eye, to see more definitively; should provide something to dilute the unsettling images in our memories.

Much has been written about Hilton Head Island. Histories and articles have been published. Slick magazine advertising has extolled golf and tennis. Billboards invite one and all to "lifetime" it here. The blare and the glare can be deafening and blinding. Turn down the volume. Hilton Head can be as calm and as restoring as you make it. Here the lights are dimmer and our five senses can come forward. Use your eyes in a new way; look closely. Touch. Hear. Taste the salt spray. Smell deeply the pure air. That is the intent of this book — to grasp Hilton Head Island by way of the senses and discover the minutiae which comprise the whole.

It has been said that life could be sustained here with a fishing line, a hoe and a shovel. The hoe could be for a row of potatoes, the shovel for oysters, and the fishing line for obvious purposes. The rest of your diet might consist of sea rocket found on the beach, buds of yucca, or boiled glasswort from the marshes. (Forgive the use of "wort." Botanists eschew euphonious sounds else how could they christen the delicate yellow orchid in our woodlands a "bladderwort"?) A word of caution: on any outdoor junket it's a good idea to look but don't touch for several reasons. Plants should be conserved; some are poisonous, and the less the environment is disturbed, the better for everything.

The Island can hold its precious secrets close to its chest but, if you are receptive, the Island can extend two hands palms up with the gifts of life.

Flex your receptivity as you leave Interstate 95, the north-south artery that pumps people on to capillary roads and into Low Country living. If you choose Highway 462, your first grove of spreading live oaks will be on your left, dominating the yard of a brick house. These oaks will become increasingly familiar to you. Some will be more heavily adorned than others in their gray veils of Spanish moss. Some will support a delicate green fern, called "Resurrection" because the fern seems to die during dry spells and is restored to life by the first rain. Plan now to locate a particular live oak, claim it and have a picnic in it, not under it.

As you drive further, look for pines which fill the once fertile fields of plantation days, some of which support the five-leafed Virginia creeper or the infamous three-leafed poison ivy. These lands sustained life on plantations owned by the likes of Thomas Heyward, a signer of the Declaration of Independence. Shortly after crossing the intersection at Big House, where the highway changes to 278, look carefully to your left for brick pillars and iron gates which are the entrance to Mr. Heyward's burial site, a truly peaceful and beautiful place, and an excellent one from which to view and smell the marshes. (To a true Islander returning home, the first smell of the salt marsh proclaims all's right with his world.)

Should you fly to the Savannah airport for your Island sojourn, put your nose on hold until after Port Wentworth and across the Savannah River. The odor that assaults your senses is the digestive system of a paper mill. An avenue of palms is evidence that the Wentworths wanted better times for their town. Ah, but the wealth of ecology as you drive through the Savannah Wildlife Refuge! Rice ranked as high as cotton as a money crop in ante-bellum days, and the Wildlife Refuge utilizes the rice dikes to control water levels just as they were used over a century ago. Aside from lotus and water lilies the wild grasses form a smorgasbord for migrating fowl. Leave the binoculars outside the suitcase, stop the car at one of the many parking spots, and walk out on one of the rice dikes. You should be rewarded with any combination of the following: gallinules, stilts, wood ducks, least bitterns, redwing blackbirds. The rest is up to you.

Now your senses should be ready to discover Hilton Head Island. Since everything has a plan, perhaps the best approach to the adventure is a counter-clockwise peripheral route of the Island, beginning with Windmill Harbour. Right away this brings us a paradox. Here much is the same and much has changed — even the name. Until recently Windmill Harbour was known as Jenkins Island. The land planner envisioned a wind-powered mill which would operate the harbor lock. Having little faith in Gertrude Stein, other designators changed Hog Bluff to Moss Creek and Horse's Hole (in Sea Pines Plantation) to Audubon Pond. Walking the woodlands of Windmill Harbour it is possible to see near the edge of the island the narrow old oyster-shell road from Old Ferry Point (exactly what the name implies). The distinct opening in the heavily wooded area was the only connector to the mainland before the first bridge was completed in 1956. Islanders, mostly in wagons or on horseback, met the excursion boat and later the ferry for mail, provisions and passengers. The swath among the trees and the sprinkling of crushed shells on the roadbed are the only visible remains of this passage. The question arises, "Why has the roadbed followed the edge when a more direct route would be straight across the island?"

An imaginative answer would be that, since one of the Island's twenty-four pre-Civil War plantations occupied Jenkins Island, the fields were cultivated and any road would necessarily follow the water's edge. No one knows where the plantation house stood, but the sleuth in us would surmise that it was near a grove of Redbud (Judas) trees. These trees are tall and skinny with heart-shaped leaves and in the spring small pink buds are visible if you turn your eyes upward.

This water walk is a great introduction to many trees and birds to be found around Hilton Head Island. Marsh lace, sassafras, wax myrtle, cassina, Cherokee bean on the high land and spartina grass and rushes in the marshes. To many, the marshes are more interesting than the beaches. Here the landscape and birdlife vary with the tides and seasons. If the tide is out and the gray mud exposed, don't walk out on it for that tempting piece of driftwood. You would sink right up to your ankles and possibly your knees. Instead, stay on dry land and listen. Yes, listen. The "poofing" sound is air escaping after being trapped in the mud by the last high tide. You might even hear an oyster spit!

To the veteran explorer, low tide in the marshes is by far a more rewarding time although high tide reflecting the sky may be more beautiful. When the tide is out, the fiddler crabs march in small armies. They've learned that it's a treat to beat your feet. Marsh hawks hover and hunt small voles that feed on grass seeds.

The myrtle and cassina bushes are most interesting around Thanksgiving when their berries flourish and make a holiday feast for the birds. Break the rule when you see a wax myrtle or bayberry shrub with lavender berries lining a branch. Pull off a few berries, crush them in your hands and the smell of bayberry candles will stir memories. The flock of small, yellow-rumped birds feasting among the branches of wax myrtle are the myrtle warblers, what else?

The guardian of the Cassina bush with its glossy red berries is the mockingbird. The mocker burns all its calories chasing jays and chickadees from its private stock. Indians used Cassina leaves to make medicinal tea at any season. Even today the Charleston Receipts cookbook has the recipe.

Sassafras trees are also the source of tea (and root-beer), but in this case boil the root instead of the dried leaves and your brew will be red instead of black.

As you drive to your next destination, Spanish Wells Plantation, observe the middens on each side of William Hilton Parkway. The inexhaustible tides have been at work depositing floating objects from boats and from other shores. Among the fishermen's floats and driftwood, Indian pottery and broken plantation glass have been found. Here and there, among the reeds, are abandoned bateaus, the native wooden flat-bottomed oyster boat. For years the bateau was rowed and poled around the creeks, but now, in most cases, small outboard motors have been added.

The Spanish well itself is a fresh-water depression not far inside the Plantation gate on the right side of the road. Old charts mark the spot where Spanish ships, beginning in 1521, filled their casks and where some fine horseflesh either escaped or were put ashore for some obscure reason thereby becoming the ancestors, combined later with plantation horses, of the marsh tackies which occasionally can be seen tethered in the yards of Islanders. Even more rare today is to see one of these horses hitched to a plow.

Along the Parkway are Chinaberry trees or as the Gullah dialect describes them, "Asa-berry." After all, the native explains, the trees came from Asia. And so did the Chinese tallow tree which is everywhere on Hilton Head Island. More commonly called the Popcorn tree because of the clusters of white, waxy berries produced in late fall, the Chinese tallow tree grows rapidly from only a switch and its leaves turn either red or orange or gold before dropping. As the name implies, the berries were used in candlemaking.

Wherever possible in this discovery of Hilton Head Island, use your bicycle or walk. Most of the developments provide excellent bike paths. In the works are Islandwide Pathways for Safety which will someday allow pedal power from the bridge down William Hilton Parkway.

The fact that Islanders must do most beneficial actions themselves contributes strongly to the Island's individuality. We scrap among ourselves and air our differences in the three local newspapers, but, with few exceptions, Islanders have a common goal of making this the best of all possible worlds. How we attain those goals adds the spice of personalities which makes living here exciting.

Hilton Head is one of the few sea islands which has been humanly habitated uninterrupted for thousands of years. Some of the Indian artifacts have been carbon dated as early as 2000 B.C. This continuity of life lends a sense of history which compels the modern-day resident to build a hospital, a library, churches, community theater, animal shelter, propose density caps and search for museum sites and a performing arts center. To the majority of Islanders these issues are far more important than how the green slopes or how the ball bounces.

Even with committees and commitments, we try never to lose sight of the natural beauty that surrounds us. We look for shapes in clouds as children would, we view incomparable sunrises and sunsets, but we also look into the sloughs and ditches where bulldozer and bird have worked together to plant cattails, arrowhead swamp potato, pickerel weed, white bracted sedge, lizard's tail and water lilies. Animals delight in the succulent new growth of cattails and roots of the swamp potato. Humans delight in seeing the small white blossoms of the potato or the purple of pickerel.

The old road on which the Stoneys and the Lawtons of plantation days drove ten miles to Zion Chapel of Ease is still visible. Part of it has been surfaced with asphalt and is now Plantation Drive and Greenwood Drive in Sea Pines Plantation. The small church, or Chapel of Ease, is gone with the wind of the Civil War, but the burial ground, prominently marked by the Baynard Mausoleum on the Parkway near Folly Field Road, is a generation by generation step back in history.

The Elizabethan word "folly" is found at least twice on Hilton Head maps: on old maps the area which is now Beach Lagoon and also a large part of Sea Pines was called Old Woman's Folly; on current maps is Folly Field. Folly meant low place as opposed to "hope" which meant a high place.

Six Oaks Cemetery, created in the 1960s, is located near the Lawton plantation house site and takes its name from the six gigantic live oaks which border the drive to the house site. Lawton Creek, meandering its tidal way, transported people and products from the plantation to Calibogue Sound. Today the cemetery has been landscaped totally with azaleas and is worth a springtime visit.

Calibogue Cay was once called Long Island and records show that citrus trees thrived on the spit of high land. Before houses thrived here elbow-to-elbow, Indian artifacts as well as fresh oysters were easily found at low tide on the Broad Creek side. Living on Calibogue Cay until the late 1960s required a deal of planning. Plantation Drive was a deeply-rutted sand road and the "gate" closed at 7 p.m. If rains came on the night of a Calibogue party, roads were impassable and cancellation notices went out.

This was also true over many other parts of the Island. Permanent equipment in the trunk of my car consisted of a tow cable, a machete, a .22 rifle and a box of scatter shot. The machete was for hiking through dense woodlands, the rifle for the occasional rattlesnake or for shooting mistletoe out of the tall oaks once a year. The tow cable was used almost daily. Finding someone stuck in the sand was as frequent as today's fender benders. Once I pulled a native's car from a sandy shoulder. The very next day he appeared at my door with a quart of butterbeans — shelled — to offer his thanks.

Gifts have always been this Island's legacy. One of these gifts was discovered and used by Indians — the Toothache tree. Calibogue Cay has one, South Beach a few and there is a large one in the parking area at Dolphin Head. A thick bark is kept free from deer scrubbings by large sharp thorns that encrust the tree's trunk. The thorn can be cut away with a knife and the base of the thorn chewed where a tooth aches. The area is anesthetized temporarily, but most dental work would still be a painful procedure.

On the south end of Calibogue Cay and to the left as you face toward Harbour Town, the tidal marsh has been arranged by the Master Artist and a varied aviary of herons is yours for the choosing, unchanged for centuries. If primitive areas are what you are seeking, approach Harbour Town by way of Deer Island. The narrow dirt track to the right as you leave the Cay is a little tough for bikes, but great for walking and identifying deer and raccoon tracks. The small houses on stilts are almost invisible and overlook some of the best views on Hilton Head Island.

Harbour Town is the extra step that land planner and developer Charles Fraser took that made him world famous and emulated by all who would remove the stigma from the word "developer." With building costs soaring in the 60s, did he need to spend extra money on a wooden bridge connecting Deer Island to Harbour Town? Did he need to slice a wedge in the harbor itself to save the Liberty Oak? Did he need to hire an artist to coordinate the colors of buildings and design two of Harbour Town's wooden structures after historical houses? These are but a few of the details which make Sea Pines Plantation the model for future developments and, yes, the prototype from which to observe errors not to be repeated.

As construction on Harbour Town was planned, Charles Fraser purchased two lighthouse-keeper houses from Palmetto Dunes. When the houses were moved to Harbour Town, an uninvited guest came along with her home. While dredges gnawed away at the harbor, a few young Islanders made nightly trips down the dirt road to visit the new resident whom they called the Blue Lady. The apparition glowed a faded indigo blue. That she was a lady is evidenced by her jealousy of at least one young girl who visited the Blue Lady's abode. The young girl was "called" up the attic steps toward the glow at the top of the stairs. The girl became hysterical when she was "pushed" back down the stairs by the indignant Lady.

The Blue Lady's presence, a breath of cold air as she passed, was last felt by an 18-year-old boy. His glance was directed downward and there, on the ground at his feet, was a thin silver wedding ring. The brick courtyard between the two houses (the site where the ring was found and now occupied by Signe's and a real estate company) was named the Court of the Blue Lady. So, you see, on Hilton Head you need to sharpen not only your five senses but your extrasensory as well.

There is mystery on the opposite side of the harbor also. Close up against a high-rise apartment building on the 18th fairway of the Harbour Town Golf Links is one of the many black cemeteries on the Island where natives have buried their dead for well over 100 years. Burials are still taking place there as recently as the 1986 Heritage Golf Classic. Despite thousands of golf spectators and the attendant traffic, a dignified procession of mourners quietly laid a friend to rest. The oldest graves will often have a cup or dish embedded in the concrete marker, a heritage from the African continent or from other cultures. Here again, look but don't touch. Foul times have been known to follow those who disturb these objects.

The Gullah dialect is thought to be a blend of West Indian English with some words from the Elizabethan era. The term probably is a corruption of the nationality of the speaker, Angolan, and the African country from which so many came. Since slaves were prevented by law from learning to read or write, Gullah is a spoken language. Words are heard only, not seen. For example, Honey Horn Plantation derives its name from Hanahan, the original owners. The Gullah heard Hanahan and ultimately the name became Honey Horn. Attempting to understand Gullah between natives is futile. It is rapid, musical and filled with strange words. It took three repetitions before I realized my friend who said, "Ah cain git de sosh up," was trying to tell me she couldn't raise the window. Sometimes the words are more than needed as the Gullah says, "All two-a-dem" instead of "both." Other times they solve the sex discrimination dilemma by saying "shem" to mean him or her. Gullah is a wondrous patois, in need of preservation, as worthy a subject of Black History as any being accredited today.

Plantation houses were always located near a waterway and even though the well-marked ruins of the Baynard house seem to sit upon a hill in a dense woodland, look around you. Some believe the "hill" was slave made, and 150 years ago the inhabitants could see the ocean on their east and Calibogue (or Long Island) Sound on their west. Look more closely to the south and follow the path that will lead you to the plantation's waterway, now only a silted-in creek. Imagine the grandeur of this tabby house, flanked by slave quarters and overlooking fields of cotton and indigo. Now look again and see that this tabby house, though in ruins, is still host to the Carolina Wren, South Carolina's state bird. The small brown bird with its perky, canted tail sings one of the birddom's most magnificent songs. Also a herd of white-tailed deer has selected these grounds as a haven. Here, as well as on Gull Point and Audubon Pond Roads, is the best deer spotting in early morning and late afternoon.

One of the great additional delights of tennis has been playing at South Beach. Not only does the ocean breeze cool the brow, but frequently an unexpected spectator in the form of a marsh rabbit might attend. These small brown rabbits have shorter ears, a sparse tail and are natually camouflaged among pine needles and tall grasses. Not so fortunate is the nervous gray squirrel which must hug the bark of trees to escape the hawk's eye. I witnessed a red-shouldered hawk swoop down for the kill on a squirrel that lingered too long in an open space. The hawk grasped the squirrel in its talons and struck one swift beak's blow on the back of the squirrel's head in one concerted action. The hawk then arched its wings like outriggers for balance and waited until the squirrel's death throes ceased. Then only did the bird fly with its prey.

Walk the South Beach at low tide and go as far around the point known as Land's End as the beach permits. That high-pitched laughter isn't a bystander ridiculing your appendages; it's the aptly named Laughing Gull. Egrets and herons enjoy fine fishing here as the tides ebb and flow. Shrimp boats anchor here, holding their nets above the waterline much like a lady in crinoline skirts. Sports fishermen head out and return at this joining of the Atlantic Ocean and Calibogue Sound. Their gear is far more sophisticated than the herons, but, if the truth were told, which of them has the greater catch?

South Beach uses all your senses. Feel the breeze on your cheeks; taste the salt on your lips; see Daufuskie Island across the inlet; smell the sea creatures at low tide; and hear the dolphins. The bottle-nosed dolphin is a constant companion at the south tip of the Island where the land falls off sharply. Listen first for the "whoosh" sound as the dolphin surfaces to expel air. He will take time out from his fishing to accompany you on your walk, smiling at you each time he surfaces. They never seem to lose their playfulness or their sense of humor. I saw one best a noisy Cocker Spaniel when the Spaniel was taken with a fit of barking on first seeing a dolphin. At the next surfacing the dolphin flipped its tail and doused the dog with sea water. Direct hit. The dog raced for the dunes, and I continued my quiet walk with a dolphin.

Seaside resorts the world over are praised for their beaches. Blue water, ivory sand, golden sea oats and green trees make ideal brochure material and Hilton Head Island stands at the top with all these attributes. Shelling may be a disappointment, but consider the calm water given to the sailor and swimmer by those same offshore sand bars which not only temper the large swells, but garner the seashells as well. The wide, smooth beaches and shallow sloping undersea floor make this a paradise for small children.

Discover all the other things this beach offers. Look for the Spanish Bayonet (Yucca) behind the dunes. In May and June Yucca can be identified by the edible creamy white blossoms which profusely line a tall spike emerging from a dangerously sharp burst of stiff, bayonet-shaped leaves. Indians used this plant like a general store. Beginning with the thick roots they made soap. Moving on up, they pounded the leaves and made sandals, ropes and mats from the leaves. While you're browsing, remember to shake any ants from the Yucca blossoms before popping them into your mouth.

Among the first line of green plants on the beach, look for Sea Rocket. The fleshy green leaves of this low-growing plant can be added to your sandwich or taken home for the evening's salad. The flat green leaves of a nearby vine is probably the Pennywort with round leaves the size of an English penny. And if the season is fall, those familiar white flowers on a creeping vine are Morning Glories. The pale violet flowers on a bush vine is the Butterfly (or Beach) Pea, while the bright pink flowers of the wild bean is a distant cousin.

Summer is the swimmers' season, but equally exciting and continually neglected is the winter beach. The atmosphere is clearer, and you will vow there are more stars in the sky. The constellation Orion's three-starred belt wraps the earth while the planets Jupiter, Mars, and Venus chase each other across the firmament. If you have never walked the beach in the rain, you owe yourself this closeness with the elements. Have a fire laid before you go out, wear your rain gear and look forward to the cup of tea or chocolate by the fire when you return.

The full-moon nights in July and August bring turtle watchers to the beach. Not many people have been fortunate enough to witness the poignancy of the Loggerhead Sea Turtle as she drags her 300-plus pounds from the sea to the high-tide line to lay her eggs. She digs a one-foot-deep crescent-shaped trench and deposits anywhere from 80 to 150 eggs that look like ping-pong balls into the trench and then laboriously covers them in an attempt to protect the eggs from predators. She sheds great tears during this act. One cannot tell whether she weeps from pain or the fact that she knows she will never see the dozen or so babies that will survive their enemies during the two-month incubation or the long, slow toddle to the sea when they hatch. But those who escape the raccoon, ghost crab, fish (and, until recently, poachers) may live 100 years. Some say that when these female babies reach maturity, they return to the same shore to lay their eggs.

On any summer night you will no doubt see one of the predators of sea-turtle eggs — the Ghost Crab. When they are not flitting swiftly across the beach, they will "freeze" and become practically invisible since they are the same color as the sand. Their burrows have entrances just about the size of the turtle egg.

THE GHOST CRAB

The eternal mists wrap the beach,
Enclosed within a milky shell
      this borderline,
A meeting of two worlds
Of life within the sand and swell.

I am a part of both of these
Inseparable at birth,
This borderland of sand and sea,
A marriage of the earth.

Flagellant life in the churning broth
Give up dominion unto me,
A vagrant crab on morning beach
Within my reach, the mothering sea.

— Jim Orr

If you were equipped with twenty-league boots, a walk on the beach all the way to Port Royal Plantation would reward you with some unusually fine landscaping of oceanfront hotels. Both the Marriott operations (Monarch in Sea Pines and the hotel in Shipyard Plantation) have set their buildings back from the beach and have commissioned water gardens which contain fountains, pools, hybrid water lilies and lotus. Not far from the Marriott Hotel is Mariner's Inn water garden on the beach at Palmetto Dunes.

The Hyatt was the first of the large hotel chains to build on Hilton Head Island and brought a bit of city glitter with the Indigo Room and large convention facilities. Their series of terraces and pools are a tribute to modern architecture.

Then there is a long span before you arrive at the newest and most costly, Hotel Inter-Continental, at Port Royal Plantation. All five of these establishments are worth a trek over the dunes to see their grounds and, if the hour and season are right, sample a libation at the poolside bars.

As you round the northeastern corner of Hilton Head Island, the Atlantic Ocean enters Port Royal Sound, the site of a very one-sided naval and shore battle between North and South in 1861. At that time it was the largest armada of Union ships ever mounted. When the smoke cleared a few hours later, the small garrison of Confederate soldiers had fled, and what is now part of Port Royal Plantation was occupied by Union troops. A town of about 50,000 people grew around the landing site, and merchants, soldiers and sailors alike were the first tourists to discover the joys of Hilton Head Island. They played baseball on the beach, established a newspaper and theater, baked their own bread and wrote glowing letters home describing citrus groves and beauties of the Island. They enjoyed their stay so much that, in four years, they neglected to carry out their orders from President Lincoln and General Sherman to cut the mainland railroad line connecting Savannah with Charleston. This possibly could have ended the Civil War much sooner.

When the garrison and its services departed, they left behind many bottles, buttons and bibelots which both professional and amateur archaeologists have unearthed. A recent "dig" at Fish Haul Plantation, sponsored by The Museum of Hilton Head Island, revealed how slaves lived in a settlement called Mitchelville shortly after being liberated. The Museum has obtained land on Main Street, Hilton Head Plantation's development off William Hilton Parkway. When funds have been raised for the building, the Museum will focus on the history and ecology of the Low Country.

Blacks have continued to live in the Mitchelville area, calling part of their settlement Beach City. They still play baseball on what must be the only Sound-front baseball diamond in the world and their team, the Bluejays, produced the National League star, Dan Driessen.

Throughout Hilton Head and Port Royal Plantations residential roads cut through Civil War redoubts. A fortunate few who purchased land near these batteries have private collections of octagonal glass inkwells, medicine and beer bottles, and an occasional gold locket from "the girl back home." The site of the failed cannon fired by steam is marked by an historic plaque and huge chunks of concrete on the beach at Port Royal. This was the War Department's answer from Washington to Spanish-American War coastal defense. The shot from the cannon was propelled all the way across Port Royal Sound and set fire to the woods at Bay Point. It was never fired again. The Marine training base at Parris Island may be seen across Port Royal Sound and when the wind is from the north, their firing can be heard.

As pointed out earlier, the configuration of Hilton Head Island has changed drastically. At Dolphin Head high bluffs reveal strata of clays, and oaks and magnolias have fallen beneath the onslaught of pounding storms. Other treasures from other centuries make Dolphin Head a beachcomber's dream. Low tide is the best time to have a good beach for walking. At high tide there isn't any. At an erosion rate of three feet per year, the bluffs that caused Captain William Hilton to name this island Hilton Head have eroded southward 250 feet since 1860, leaving William Elliott's Myrtle Bank plantation house foundations in the Sound. The tabby ruins may be seen at low tide. Almost every walk will produce some souvenir: a piece of old brick from plantation days, a small bit of Indian pottery (identifiable by one burnt side and the other side usually etched by reed in distinctive patterns), a piece of blue and white plantation china, or, if the spirits are truly walking with you, a flint spearpoint or tool. Should you be so lucky, hold the flint tightly and try to imagine the difficulty the Indian had in producing this hunting instrument.

There are no indigenous rocks on Hilton Head Island. Indians hollowed out the huge oak and magnolia trunks to make dugout canoes, their only means of contact with the mainland and other parts of the Island. Imagine the men loading these boats with foodstuffs and game to be traded for flint on the mainland. Many trading sites are along the Savannah River where large pieces of flint were pounded into smaller ones for easier transport home. These arrow and spearpoints must have been lifetime treasures, retrieved again and again. Abundant oyster shells provided excellent, sharp, cutting and scraping tools once the game was slain.

All along the shoreline of Skull Creek from Dolphin Head is evidence of human habitation through the centuries. A stop at Old Fort Pub will permit a wandering around an earth fort and along a board-walk near creek level under and around some magnificent live oaks. Most of the shrimpers dock their boats along this creek. Hudson's Seafood Restaurant and The Landings usually have a shrimp boat or two nearby. The "season" usually runs from June through December and watching the unloading and cleaning is fascinating.

One of two Indian Shell Rings on the Island is on Squire Pope Road, but it is on private land. An easier access and a larger site is in the Sea Pines Forest Preserve. So let's backtrack to the south end; this time to the interior. Parking is at two entrances: one on Greenwood Drive shortly after entering the Greenwood gate, and another off Lawton Road. My favorite approach is the latter because you immediately begin to see wildlife at this entrance.

Remember the little brown marsh rabbit? He may be racing along in front of you, for burrows are on either side of the entrance path which you will recognize as a rice dike. To your right is a drainage ditch, not a very pretty name for what becomes a favorite waterway for migrating fowl. Pause for a moment on a bench provided just for this, let your eyes adjust and you may see a purple gallinule walking on lily pads, turning them over and peering underneath for tender morsels.

Listen for the sounds of the alligator. If he makes any noise at all, or even moves, give him plenty of room. He hisses if he is angry or protective and bellows (like a fog horn) if he wants to mate. Either action could be most unwelcome, and, contrary to his heavy, lethargic appearance, the 'gator can move very fast. Generally he picks on something smaller than he — small dogs, for example — using his powerful tail as a club and drowning his victim.

The Forest Preserve is exactly what the name implies. Published figures vary as to its size, but the Preserve does include hundreds of acres. Take your tree and bird books along. All the trees and bushes mentioned in this book are here in abundance and the centerpiece is the very large Indian shell ring. Nature seems to have chosen this place for a special garden.

Buckeye, a small tree, blooms in the spring, rather nondescript, but the large, rounded brown seeds are coveted as good-luck charms. Although a large grove of Buckeye trees flourishes beside the shell ring, finding a seed is a real discovery. Something seems to spirit them away.

The circle of mounded oyster shells is host to the lance-leafed violet which sends up its pale lavender, almost white, blooms in early spring. In the center of the circle, standing so tall as to be unnoticed by some, is one of several species of Magnolia (the Bay family) found on the Island. This particular giant does not branch until about fifteen feet above the ground and the enormous trunk brings to mind a totem.

The mystery of Indian shell rings remains shrouded, but it is generally agreed that the uniformity of the circle denotes a meeting place, possibly ceremonial. Why, you may ask, would Indians transport oysters and shells to the middle of the woods? The sleuth that must have been developing as you discover Hilton Head would immediately answer that, with constantly changing contours, this area was at one time on or near the shoreline. Indians that inhabited Hilton Head Island were hunters, gardeners and lived in villages. They used the creeks, faster and easier than overland, and their gathering places would necessarily be close to a waterway.

Proceeding still farther on the wide pathways of the Forest Preserve, we come to a large, man-made central lake. Planting of special grasses nearby has attracted migrant ducks, and fishing is a favorite pastime. A small area is provided for cleaning, grilling, and picnicking. Cypress trees have been planted on the banks of the lake.

On the opposite side of the lake, a pathway leads to boardwalks of Vanishing Swamp which was created by lowering water tables and natural buildup of vegetation. Beyond the swamp is nature's playground. Grapevines are large enough for swinging. By all means, do. Muscadine, the Island's wild grape, was successfully crossed with selected wine quality grapes by American vintner, Greyton Taylor, on a forty-acre experimental vineyard on Hilton Head Island some twenty years ago. Mr. Taylor also planted and tended a southern scuppernong grafted to a white, wine grapevine which produced, in its second year, at least thirty pounds of quality grapes, attesting to a possible new industry for the area. This particular grapevine was in the yard of a friend and provided a lush canopy for a small terrace. In the midst of this flourishing experiment, Greyton Taylor died and, like the grandfather clock which stopped, the friend's grapevine died also.

Not far from the grapevine swings, a vast bog contains a variety of water plants, among them (again in early spring) the bog iris, an ancestor of the Dutch iris. Occasionally the alert discoverer will spot these plants in the ditches around the Island.

Perhaps this is the best time to talk about some of the Island trees not already mentioned. Fall here does not display the leaf color that causes people to tour New England and the mountains in this season, but sometimes in November the huge hickories turn the rich tone of museum-quality gold; sassafras produces about 14 karat; black gum changes to varied colored rubies, and the swamp maple still hangs on to its pinkish-red leaves first evidenced in its spring buds.

Yes, Hilton Head Island does have seasons which in themselves have attracted many to make this a permanent home. Most people use spring-weight woolens for December, January and February; keep the sweaters out for March and April; begin swimming in May and continue through September; then October and November are repeats of March and April. No one truly puts away the summer cottons because any mid-winter day might whimsically warm to the 70s.

It is rare to hear an Islander comment on the first day of spring, fall, summer or winter, as far as the calendar reads. But hearing of the return of a certain bird and that it must be April 10 is an annual thing. That bird is the Painted Bunting and may be seen on the coast as far north as Charleston. Perhaps you have seen this flying prism, a little smaller than a Bluebird. Some call them little flying rainbows, but one person described it well when he said, "Looks like it was made from spare parts from a Macaw factory." Whatever you do (from April to October), if you don't see one of these marvels in the wild, ask around for someone who has attracted them to a birdfeeder. Island hospitality will certainly invite you to the show. By early October the Painted Bunting has returned to Mexico and Central America.

What is an island without palm trees? Many Hilton Head residents describe their bit of property by cataloguing three items: location, view and type of trees. One very proud owner claimed sixteen palm trees. Lucky fellow, for on any breezy night, the wind in the palms sounds for all the world like light rain.

Actually the "palms" here are Palmetto trees. This tree centers the South Carolina state flag on a field of blue and figures historically in the defense of its fortresses. Cannonballs sank deep and harmlessly into the Palmetto's soft pulpy trunk. Mature Palmettos can reach a height of sixty feet, and their leathery, drooping fronds (up to six feet long) could certainly roof your little grass shack. Don't confuse the tall Palmetto with the Saw Palmetto which grows nearby in shrub clusters to a height of about five feet. This shrub is aptly named, for the stem of its fronds can certainly saw into skin. Landscapers have all but given up eliminating this shrub in yards. The roots run laterally and pop up every few inches with fresh green shoots. The sharp-spined fronds provide excellent cover against predators for deer, snakes and birds.

For a century one animal was impervious to the pricks and sticks of all Island flora. The feral pig, gone back to nature after the farms and plantations were no longer flourishing, became larger and larger until, by the late 1950s, it became known as the wild boar on the Island. The wide breastplate made the boar a natural enemy of the poisonous snake, and as its snout became longer and the tusks more dominant, the boar or wild pig, became an enemy of man. As golf courses were developed, the pig would come by night and dig up what man had created by day. Heavy wooden traps were made to capture the three- or four-hundred pound animal. If you were brave enough, a seat in one of the live oaks in what is now Lawton Woods would soon provide you with a good look at one of these ferocious beasts. The last ones were seen on the Island about 1972.

One transplanted New Yorker got too good a look at a boar as it came from cover to chase her dog. Both she and her dog were fast enough to escape to a nearby fairway where, looking back to see if the boar had stayed in the woods, she stumbled over an eight-foot alligator asleep in the sun. Her breathless remark was, "I'll have you know that, until today, I've never seen anything wilder than a cockroach." She has never returned to the woodlands.

As you wander elsewhere more perceptively now after your adventure on Hilton Head Island, perhaps you are more aware of God's great plan, how He gave us wisdom and reason, and evened the score by giving animals instinct and protective coloration.

The Chuck-will's-widow wins first prize in camouflage. I have stood within six feet of this pigeon-sized bird when she was on her nest in a habitual place — the ground. If she hadn't flushed, I would never have seen her or the two eggs she temporarily abandoned. In the ensuing weeks I visited the area daily, keeping at least ten yards away and using binoculars. Even with careful "marking" in my mind with identifying sticks and grasses, I still found it difficult to see her on the nest. The speckled brown feathers blended perfectly with the surrounding pine needles.

The Chuck-will's-widow is a night bird, hunting and mating in the dark. After her two chicks, the size of baby ducks, were hatched, I went back to the nest at night, hoping for a flashlight view of the babies while Mama was hunting for food. No way. Mama swooped like a bat to let me know this was off limits at all hours.

Wild birds and animals can become accustomed to human beings. Wild birds have been trained to eat from human hands, but it takes much patience. Should you see any wild creature, continue as you were, walking or talking. To stop and point puts the wild one on alert to two possible menaces, the pointed object and the eye.

More often than realized, the hunted is watching the hunter. Think of it when you pass a tall stand of grass. Perhaps the deer are watching you. Or the raccoon, even a bobcat, is peering down from a crotch in a tree. Continue with your discoveries, but remember that peaceful co-existence is necessary for the preservation of all living species.

WILLIAM CORNELIA

Bill Cornelia is a native of Rochester, New York, and a graduate of Rochester Institute of Technology. Before moving to Hilton Head Island in 1971 he operated his own photographic studio in Pittsburgh, Pennsylvania. In 1975 he co-published the book "Hilton Head Island — A Perspective" with Richard H. Rutt and the late Gary K. Chapman. In 1983 Mr. Cornelia and his wife Lois co-published the book "Hilton Head Island — Images." He currently operates a free-lance photographic business on Hilton Head Island.

MARGARET GREER

Margaret Greer is a native South Carolinian whose love affair with the Low Country began when she was ten years old. At that time she was visiting her father's home place where moss hung from great oaks, and white sand floored swamp-water swimming holes. Twenty-five years passed before she made her dream of living in such a place a reality by moving to Hilton Head Island in 1961. She was among the first contributors to *Islander* magazine and later became editor and co-publisher of the monthly magazine. She wrote a weekly column and feature articles for *The Island Packet* and has been published in regional and national magazines. In 1983 she founded and is co-owner of Lexart, Ltd., and contributes the writing and promotional half of that corporation.

Drew
the Screw

MATTIA CERATO

Holiday House / New York

To Vale, my family and all the people
who always supported me

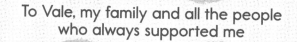 is a registered trademark of Holiday House, Inc.

Copyright © 2016 by Mattia Cerato
All Rights Reserved
HOLIDAY HOUSE is registered in the U.S. Patent and Trademark Office.
Printed and Bound in November 2015 at Tien Wah Press, Johor Bahru, Johor, Malaysia.
The artwork was created with digital tools.
www.holidayhouse.com
First Edition
1 3 5 7 9 10 8 6 4 2

Library of Congress Cataloging-in-Publication Data
Cerato, Mattia, author, illustrator.
Drew the screw / Mattia Cerato. — First edition.
pages cm. — (I like to read)
Summary: The saw cuts, the hammer hits, and the drill
makes holes; so Drew needs a job too.
ISBN 978-0-8234-3540-1 (hardcover)
[1. Screws—Fiction. 2. Tools—Fiction.] I. Title.
PZ7.C3186Dr 2016
[E]—dc23
2015015546

ISBN 978-0-8234-3541-8 (paperback)

I am Drew the screw.

I live here.

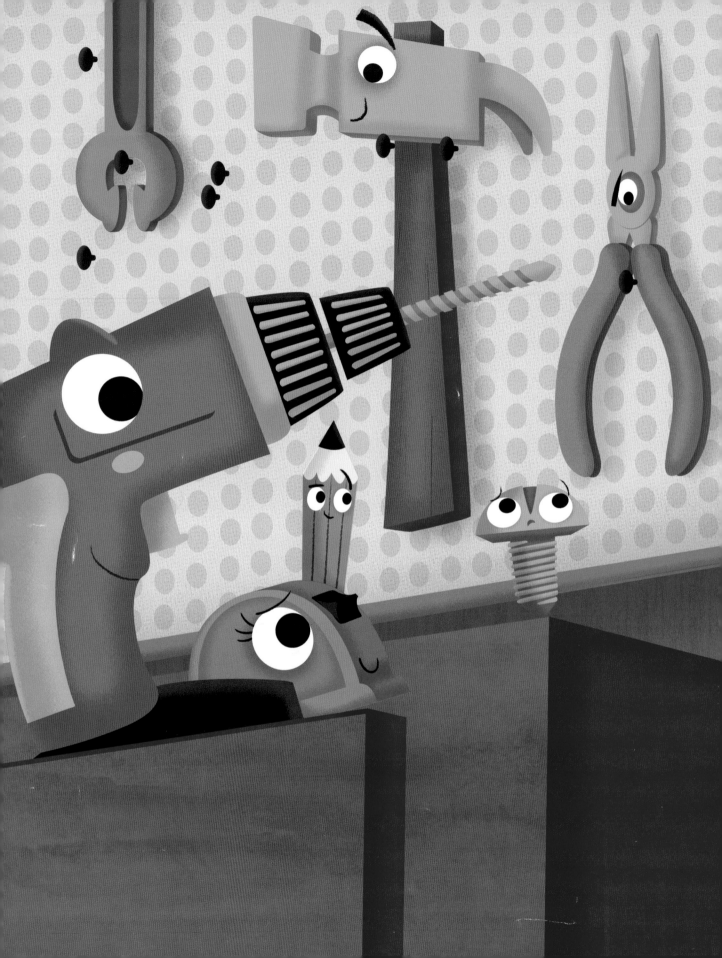

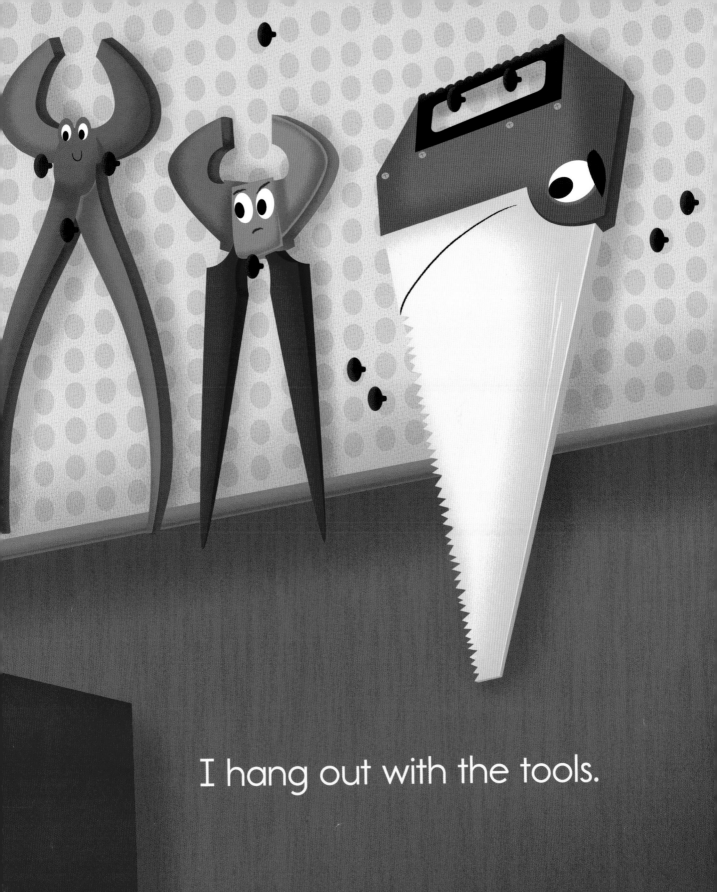

I hang out with the tools.

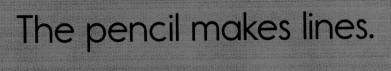
The pencil makes lines.

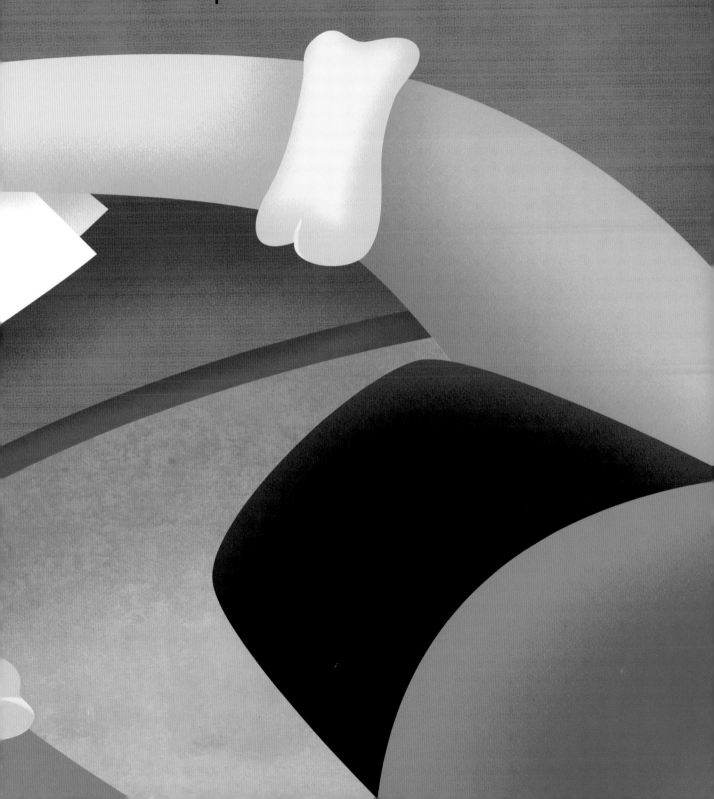

The tape measures.

The saw cuts.

The hammer hits.

The clamp
holds things.

The drill makes holes.

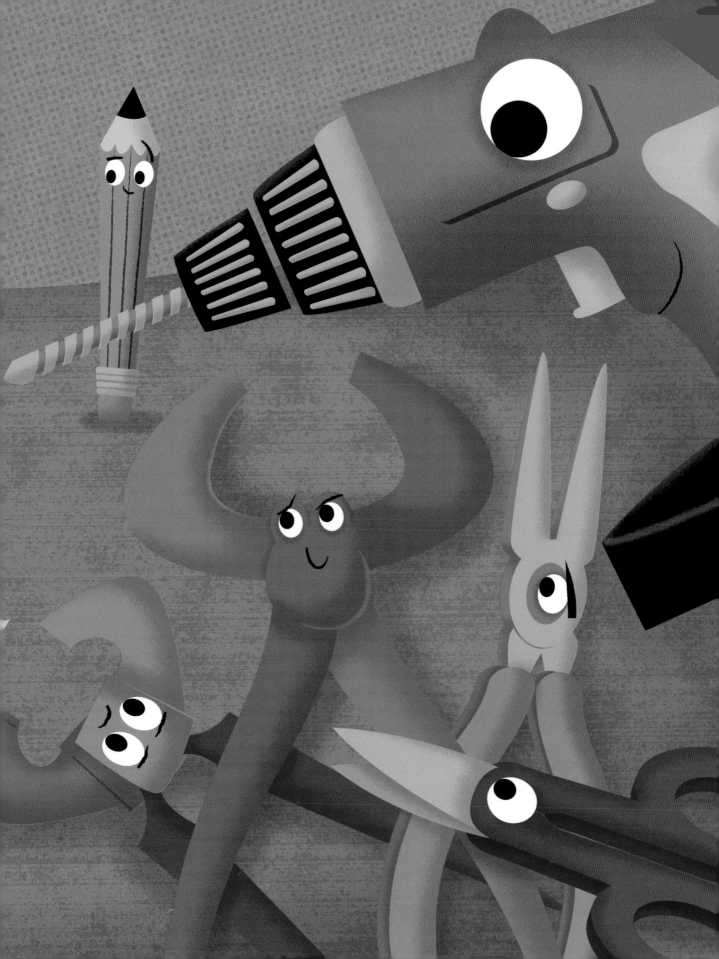

The boy has come for me.

We go up.

Now I have a job
to do too.

You will like these too!

Come Back, Ben by Ann Hassett and John Hassett
A *Kirkus Reviews* Best Book

Dinosaurs Don't, Dinosaurs Do by Steve Björkman
A Notable Social Studies Trade Book for Young People
An IRA/CBC Children's Choice

Fish Had a Wish by Michael Garland
A *Kirkus Reviews* Best Book
A Top 25 Children's Books list book

The Fly Flew In by David Catrow
An IRA/CBC Children's Choice
Maryland Blue Crab Young Reader Award Winner

Look! by Ted Lewin
The Correll Book Award for Excellence
in Early Childhood Informational Text

Me Too! by Valeri Gorbachev
A Bank Street Best Children's Book of the Year

Mice on Ice by Rebecca Emberley and Ed Emberley
A Bank Street Best Children's Book of the Year
An IRA/CBC Children's Choice

Pig Has a Plan by Ethan Long
An IRA/CBC Children's Choice

See Me Dig by Paul Meisel
A *Kirkus Reviews* Best Book

See Me Run by Paul Meisel
A Theodor Seuss Geisel Award Honor Book
An ALA Notable Children's Book

You Can Do It! by Betsy Lewin
A Bank Street Best Children's Book of the Year,
Outstanding Merit

See more I Like to Read® books.
Go to www.holidayhouse.com/I-Like-to-Read/